SANTA vs RU

Allan Plenderleith

ЯR
RAVETTE PUBLISHING

This edition published in Great Britain by
Ravette Publishing Limited 2010
PO Box 876, Horsham, West Sussex RH12 9GH

ISBN: 978-1-84161-351-2

Although he couldn't talk,
Rudolf had learned to communicate
using his antlers.

Santa teaches Rudolf
not to go hunting for his
Christmas presents.

Once again on Christmas Eve, Santa is stopped by the police.

Santa was fed up with the rising fuel prices.

Rudolf couldn't understand why it was always
Cupid that got the girls.

Santa noticed kids' Christmas
lists have changed over the years.

Where Santa takes poorly elves.

Someone had misspelt the advert for replacement elves.

Santa's favourite pizza.

The doctor reassured Rudolf he did not
in fact have gangrenous testicles, just a couple of
brussel sprouts stuck to his fur.

Once again, Rudolf had swallowed the icing bag nozzle.

Brown rain on Christmas Eve could mean only one thing:
Rudolf had the squits.

Once again, the elves' trip to Alton Towers ends in tears.

After repeated banging and a loud CRACK, Santa's door finally closed.

When Santa went to the red light district.

Santa makes his delivery
to the Chav district.

When Santa went
on Jerry Springer.

Unfortunately, Santa hadn't backed up the children's emails.

Santa's self-made winter hot-tub for helpless robins was clearly faulty.

After Randy's antics last year,
Santa came prepared.

Santa had a strange feeling Rudolf had begun to like the whip.

As the fire was dying out, Santa asks Rudolf
to chuck on some more coal.

Suddenly, Santa is caught in a tractor beam.

Santa gets political.

Santa pimps his ride.

To increase his maximum speed, Santa takes a tip
from pro cyclists.

Having received several complaints from locals,
Santa sorts out his "litter problem".

Midway through their journey, Santa got a flat.

Suddenly Santa realised it had been a mistake to replace Blitzen with Leroy the donkey.

Things just weren't the same since **Santa** got sponsorship.

Not everyone thinks global warming is a bad thing.

It wasn't so much the poo in his slipper that bothered Santa,
more the smirk on Rudolf's face.

My! You lookin' _fine_! You been workin' out!? Oooheee!!

Nigel the brown nose reindeer.

Santa regretted replacing the
reindeer with a Windows PC.

Santa knew Rudolf was healthy because he had a lovely wet nose.

When Santa got a stuck up chimney.

Santa discovers that not
having had sex for
a whole year can have its
disadvantages.

As the light came on, Santa realised he wasn't the only
fat person in the room with a big beard.

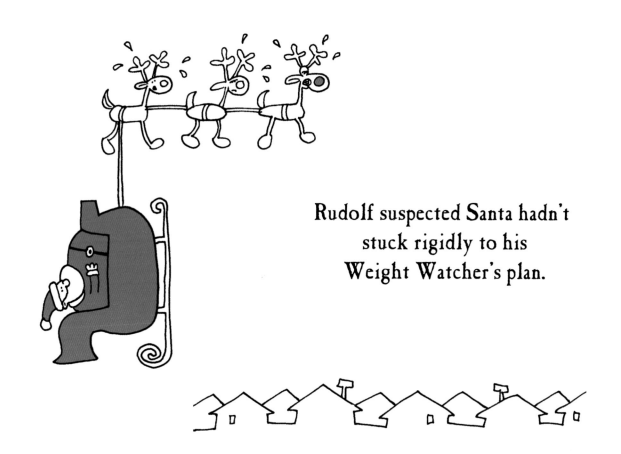

Rudolf suspected Santa hadn't
stuck rigidly to his
Weight Watcher's plan.

Unfortunately, Santa's eyesight wasn't what it used to be.

Santa made sure he always invited Rudolf
to the snooker club.

Santa got his round done much faster ever since
he introduced vindaloo to the reindeer's diet.

Maude shook off the feeling she was being watched - safe in the knowledge she was 20 storeys high.

Last year, Santa came early.

Every year, Santa dreads his visit to the Single Women's Club.

Uh oh, the kid had woken up. Santa thanked God for red wallpaper.

THUNK!

Rudolf was going bald.

Rudolf had a terrible feeling that last fart had followed through.

Rudolf learns never to sit down on icy pavements.

Not having a chimney, Billy couldn't help wonder how Santa was going to get inside.

After years of over-excited kids having 'little accidents',
Santa finally takes precautions.

Sadly, the credit crunch had even hit Santa.

The moment when
Billy became life member
of the naughty list.

Everyone on the naughty list gets a little something extra from Santa on Christmas Eve.

When Santa forgot to turn off his ringtone.

Unbeknownst to Billy,
he had discovered
'Naughty-Cam'.

Billy had actually asked Santa for an '18' video.

It wasn't until the light came on that Santa realised this wasn't in fact a downstairs toilet.

Rudolf had been much better behaved on the reins ever since Santa had tied them somewhere else.

Unfortunately, Santa's invention was not a hit
with the dragons.

Judging by all the 'chocolate kisses' on the floor, it looked like Rudolf's bum was in need of a wash again.

Suddenly Santa wished he hadn't come back for his hat.

With the help of a couple of spare elves,
Mrs. Claus gets a perky new look.

Chucky the Elf would soon get the shock of his life, as Mrs. Claus mistakes him for her "personal vibrating massager".

Santa's fur-trimmed suit had an unfortunate side-effect.

Santa couldn't understand what the elves were complaining about - after all, he'd given them a raise.

Santa would soon
discover it was his
lucky night.

Unfortunately, that last mince pie was just too much for Santa.

Mrs. Claus should have known better than to ask her
husband for stockings for Christmas.

Because of the warmer winters, Santa had to adapt his outfit.

Once again, Santa had put
his hat in with the white wash.

Whilst working on the PC, Santa had a problem with his server.

Unfortunately, it would be
some time before Rudolf noticed
Santa was missing.

Santa had actually asked his wife to check out his giant icicles.

Suddenly, Santa becomes suspicious.

Eating a million mince pies in one night had its consequences.

Clearly Santa's new sofa wasn't fire retardant.

Unfortunately there was one person Santa had forgotten to get a present for.

Santa's favourite delivery comes at the end of his round.

Once again, Santa had slept in.